Fisher Educational Ltd

Fisher Educational Ltd is a company devoted to improving mathematics and learning through its websites 10Tickers.com, 10Ticks.co.uk, 10Ticks.co.za, 10Ticks.com.au, 10Ticks.com.my, 10Ticks.com and BoffinSquad.co.uk.

Words by Jik, Jean Fisher and Ian Fisher, a mother and son writing team.

Illustrations by Emma Knowles
www.cartoonillustration.co.uk

First published 2020.

10 9 8 7 6 5 4 3 2 1

British Library Cataloguing in Publication Data.

A catalogue record for this book is available from the British Library.

ISBN: 978-1-912492-03-9

How to use this book

The experiences and activities contained within this book are intended to enable your child to develop confidently, learn effectively and become ready for school.

Numeracy and reading concepts are introduced sequentially and progressively. They go hand in hand with play experiences and are not intended to replace these valuable, first-hand play experiences of early learning.

Use the books in short, regular, frequent sessions (until your child's interest wanes), rather than occasional, lengthy ones.

When necessary, help your child to read these books and understand the mathematics and reading involved. Draw attention to the difference between each number and each letter and their names. Use the flash cards at the back of each book to help you. When ready, teach the correct formation of letters and numbers.

From the outset, when your child is interested, teach the correct way to hold a tool, (i.e. pencil, crayon, paintbrush and scissors).

Help him/her to trace some of the simple pictures.

Draw letters and numbers in sand or in the air. Use plasticine to make letters and numbers.

There are free worksheets you can use with your child if you register at www.10Tickers.com.

Some jingles and rhymes are intended for you to chant and/or dance with him/her, so that he/she feels the rhythm and beat involved. Enjoy the movement and sing/dance together.

Reinforce these learning tasks and extend the relevant vocabulary by using articles from newspapers, comics, magazines and everyday objects.

As a bonus feature, find the hidden QR codes. These codes lead to online games and activities. The one below gives an extended version of these notes. A suitable tablet device and an internet connection are required.

Ticker 4

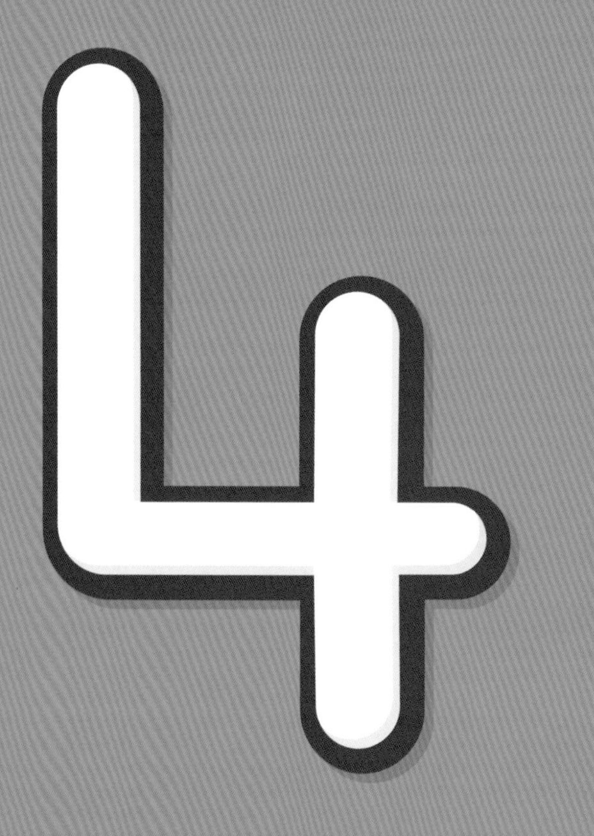

Hello.
I am
Ticker 4.

4 4 4

I am **green**.

I have a name.
It is
Ticker Four.

Four.
Four.
Four.

I have 4 green buttons.
Find my 4 green buttons.

I am in my bedroom.

Look at my buttons.

They are **circles**.

Here are Tickers 1, 2 and 3.

What **shapes** are the Tickers' buttons?

I have some new bedroom curtains.

They have shapes on them.

The Tickers want to see what is inside Ticker 4's bedroom.

Look at my curtains.

What shapes can you see?

Look at my new rug.

How many

red **circles**,

green **triangles**

and
yellow **squares** are there?

We are going on a flower hunt in the garden.

Can you find

1 square,

2 circles,

3 triangles?

Look. What has the cat got?

He's got some flags!

Red, blue, yellow and green flags.

Look at the flags.

How many circles are green?

How many triangles are yellow?

How many squares are red?

This shape has 4 **sides** all the same.

This shape has 3 sides all the same.

Tell me, tell me, what are their names?

This shape goes
round
and round
and round
and round
and round
and round
and round.

Put both hands together and point to the sky.
Stretch them, stretch them, so very, very high.

You have made a triangle.

Curl up tight into a little round ball.

You have made a circle, very, very small.

Sing and Dance time!

Put your shapes right in.

Put your shapes right out.

In, out, in, out and

shake them all about.

Do the Shapey, Shapey

and turn around.

That's what it's all about!

YES!

four

The End

Books in the series

Ticker 1 book	1	
Ticker 2 book	2	
Ticker 3 book	3	
Ticker 4 book	4	
Ticker 5 book	5	
Ticker 6 book	6	
Ticker 7 book	7	
Ticker 8 book	8	
Ticker 9 book	9	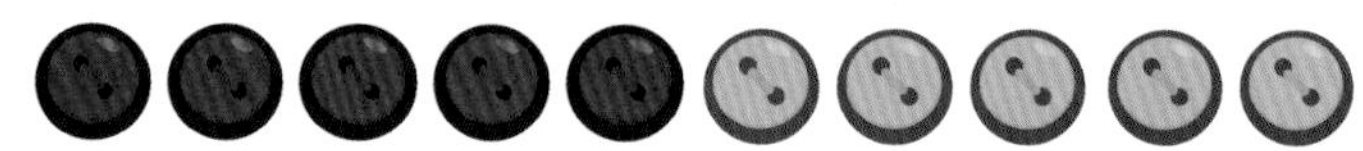
Ticker 10 book	10	
Ticker 0 book	0	